SEALIFE IN
GUERNSEY
SARK HERM AND ALDERNEY

A little souvenir by Sue Daly

CHRIS ANDREWS PUBLICATIONS

Fan coral

SEALIFE IN

GUERNSEY

SARK HERM AND ALDERNEY

Visitors to Guernsey or her neighbouring Channel Islands of Sark, Herm and Alderney can not help but be amazed by the sea here. Whether lapping lazily on golden sand in summer or pounding the cliffs with great green waves in winter, the sea pervades much of island life. In the past it carried smugglers who wrought their trade between the myriad rocky coves and the nearby coast of France. Pirates skulked on the smaller islands waiting to pounce on passing ships heading for the English Channel. Through the age of sail then steam merchants made their fortunes on goods traded by sea and many more earned their living by fishing. Over the centuries hundreds have lost their lives in these waters, victims of the swirling tides, treacherous rocks or simple human error.

Today the sea still plays an essential role in island life. Fishing remains a way of life to many islanders, whether for business or pleasure, and thousands of tonnes of cargo arrive by ship every week. Locals and visitors rely on the sea for transport, particularly during foggy weather which can paralyze the islands' airports for days at a time. More than ever the sea around the Channel Islands is a playground. Be it the challenge of riding the waves from a surf board, pottering along the coast in a sailing boat or simply relishing the sunset reflected in water, the sea lures us all.

Warmed by the Gulf Stream and pounded by Atlantic storms, the sea around the Channel Islands is home to a diverse and beautiful array of marine life. Lying almost a hundred miles

Diver exploring the Gouliot Caves

south of the English coast, some of the sea creatures here are rarely found around the British mainland. Just a few minutes peering beneath the waving fronds of seaweed in a rock pool will be rewarded with a glimpse of all sorts of fascinating marine life. A stroll along the strand line will yield a wealth of intricately patterned sea shells, each one a tiny work of nature's art.

As a scuba diver I'm privileged to venture beneath the waves and to meet the marine life in its own element. Whether swimming through a swaying forest of kelp or drifting through an anemone-smothered sea cave, there is never a shortage of wildlife to admire. The sheer rock walls are encrusted

The Lobster, the best-known crustacean in the Channel Islands with colourful sponges and corals while cuttlefish, scallops and flatfish lie camouflaged in the rolling shingle banks. Shipwrecks too are a haven for marine life, be it shimmering shoals of fish swirling around the rusting remains or crabs and conger eels lurking in the darkest holes. As on land, each habitat has its own palette of flora and fauna and, after several thousand dives in these waters, I'm still seeing creatures I've never noticed before. The photographs in this book represent just a fraction of the fabulous marine life in the waters around Guernsey, Sark, Herm and Alderney. From tiny, multicoloured sea slugs and anemones to the largest fish and sapphire blue lobsters, these creatures deserve our fullest admiration and protection.

Sea Urchin

Oyster Point and the north west coast of Herm

potential predators, the cuttlefish releases a cloud of ink and jets away behind its cover. During courtship, the male impresses his mate with a flickering display of stripes and iridescent colour. Competing males try to out shine each other with rippling flashes of patterns. After laying her eggs the female is exhausted and most mate only once, dying soon after.

The brittle white remains of a cuttlefish cast up on the shore is an internal skeleton that once housed a complex gas system for controlling the animal's position underwater. With an enormous brain and highly developed eyes, the cuttlefish is a formidable hunter. Able to move at lightning speed and change colour to blend perfectly with its background, it has a strong parrot-like beak quite capable of crushing the shell of the toughest crab. To confuse

Close-up of a Cuttlefish eye

A male Cuttlefish displaying his stripes

12   Thongweed and Kelp

Elephant's Hide Sponge

Boring Sponge

14   Yellow Hedgehog Sponge

Beadlet Anemones in the Gouliot Caves, Sark

Sponges and anemones share the characteristic of often not being recognised as living creatures but there the similarity ends. Sponges are the simplest of marine animals lacking a central nervous system or any organs. They grow in a variety of shapes and feed by filtering tiny particles of food from the water. In comparison, anemones are highly developed and armed with a battery of stinging cells deadly to any small creature that ventures within reach of their tentacles. With their gem-like hues they are among the most colourful creatures in these seas.

Jewel Anemone

Strawberry Anemone

Jewel Anemones can reproduce by budding so often cover huge areas of reef wall.

18   Yellow Cluster Anemones are colonial with a number of polyps growing from a single base.

The polyps of Devonshire Cup Corals emerge from a hard, calcareous skeleton.

20   Sunset Cup Coral is a southern species rarely found around the British mainland.

Red Sea Fingers is a hand-sized species of soft coral

Tube worms grow within a flexible, leathery tube to protect their vulnerable soft bodies. Their feathery tentacles are often beautifully striped and coloured and collect particles of food for the worm as well as acting as the animal's gills. When disturbed the tentacles are rapidly withdrawn then slowly spiral out again when the danger has passed.

Corals are most often associated with tropical seas but there are at least eight species thriving in the cool, clear waters of the Channel Islands. They are members of the same family as anemones and jellyfish and like their relatives are often brightly coloured. Cup corals live as solitary polyps blossoming from a stony skeleton attached to the reef walls. Soft coral grows as a gelatinous body supporting hundreds of feeding polyps. Each one has eight tiny tentacles that catch particles of food swept past in the blizzard of plankton.

Peacock Tube Worm

Double Spiral Worm

Rocky coast and fishing boats at Cobo, Guernsey

26   Lobsters stay hidden by day, emerging from their holes to feed at dusk

Crustaceans come in many shapes, sizes and colours but they all have one thing in common; a soft body protected by a hard shell. To grow the old shell is shed and the animal emerges with just a rubbery covering. Vulnerable without its coat of armour, it must hide for several days until the new shell hardens. Hermit crabs only have shell on their claws and the front part of their bodies so must hide their delicate soft tails in empty sea shells. As they grow they simply need to find a larger home. Crustaceans have been the mainstay of Channel Island fishermen for centuries who specifically target lobsters and the larger crabs. Restrictions on the size of animals that can be taken and the design of the pots help protect these valuable stocks.

Spider Crab

Hermit Crab at home in a Whelk shell

30   Long-clawed Squat Lobster

Masked Crab

Crawfish

32 The Shore Crab, the most common crustacean in rock pools

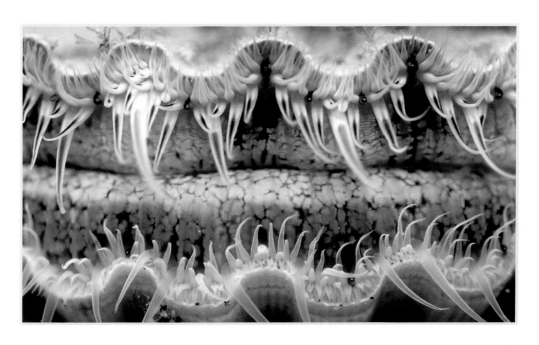

A Scallop reveals its eyes, shiny black dots, when feeding.

34   The Painted Topshell, also known as a Mermaid's Nipple!

Sea slugs are such colourful and elaborate creatures that it is difficult to believe they are related to the dull and troublesome garden slug. Known correctly as nudibranchs, which means naked gill, few of them have common names. Most are smaller than a thumb but all are carnivores grazing on tiny animals and sometimes even each other.

38   Rough sea at Vazon Bay, Guernsey

Tranquility at Saye Bay, Alderney

Pollack

More than one hundred species of fish have been
recorded in the waters around the Channel Islands
and their varying colours and shapes reflect the
part of the sea they live in. Those in mid water are
fast swimming and muscular with silvery hues
while flat fish are mottled to blend with the seabed
where they feed. Pipefish and Seahorses merge
perfectly with seaweeds while the John Dory is well
enough protected by its crown of spines that it can
live in the open. The most colourful fish are the
Cuckoo Wrasse who form harems of several
females protected by a single male. Should
anything happen to the male the oldest female will
change sex and colour and take his place
therefore all are born as females.

The colours of the male Cuckoo Wrasse (above) and the female (right) are so different that scientists originally
42 thought them to be two separate species

Female Cuckoo Wrasse

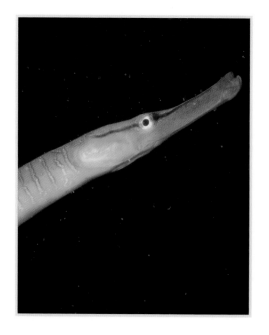

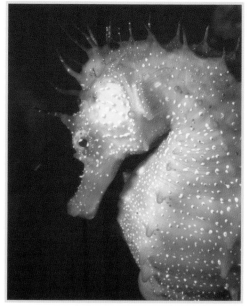

Snake Pipefish

Long-snouted Seahorse

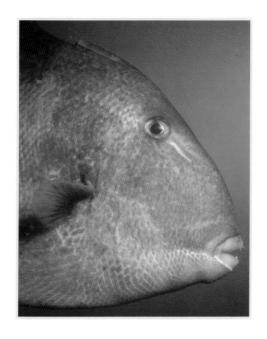

Triggerfish

John Dory

46   The Tompot Blenny, a common resident in rocky areas and on shipwrecks

The Red Gurnard feeds at night searching for prey with its feelers

48   The Conger Eel can grow to more than three metres in length

Plaice, the only flatfish with orange spots

50   Sole, a local delicacy

Shipwrecks provide divers with a fascinating mixture of history and marine life

52 The stinging tentacles of these jellyfish can reach almost a metre long

By-the-wind Sailors are occasionally blown into Channel Island waters from warmer seas.

Although they look very different, starfish and sea urchins are very closely related both belonging to the echinoderm family, which means spiny skin. They are grazers, moving around the seabed on tiny extendable legs called tube feet, a method of propulsion unique to this group of animals. Tiny suckers on the end of each tube provide enough grip to allow the creatures to move across vertical or even overhanging surfaces.

The Shore Urchin lives in the shallows and can be found in rock pools

The Sunstar feeds on starfish, even other Sunstars.

Corblets Bay, Alderney

58   The Spiny Starfish grows up to 70cm feeding on shellfish such as Scallops

Common Urchins appear in a variety of colours including pink, green, mauve and white

Sea squirts are found in harbours, rock pools and all depths of the sea but, because of their small size and apparent lack of movement, are often overlooked. They live in colonies or as separate individuals, depending on the species, but all are basically cylindrical with two openings. One draws in water which is filtered through the animal's net-like internal organ to collect food particles. The used water is then ejected through the second opening. When disturbed a sea squirt rapidly contracts its body causing the water inside to squirt out, hence its family name.

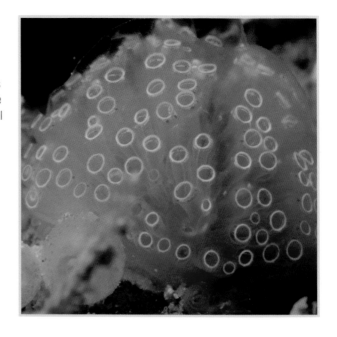

Sea Squirt

62 Sark's Guliot headland and caves with Brecqhou Island

Venus Pool, Sark

Produced by Chris Andrews Publications

Tel: +44(0)1865 723404 email: chris.andrews1@btclick.com **www: cap-ox.com**

In association with Gateway Publishing Ltd Sark

ISBN 978-1-905385-65-2

Photographed by Sue Daly with Chris Andrews. Text Sue Daly.

Front Cover: Shell Beach, Herm; Male Cuckoo Wrasse; Lobster; Sea Urchin

Back Cover: Jewel Anemones

Title Page: Jewel Anemones